KID'S TRAVEL GUIDE TO
BOSTON

A MUST HAVE TRAVEL BOOK FOR KIDS WITH BEST PLACES TO VISIT, FUN FACTS, ACTIVITIES, GAMES, AND MORE!

Dylanna Travel Press

Published by Dylanna Travel Guides and imprint of Dylanna Publishing, Inc.
Copyright © 2019 by Dylanna Travel Guides

Editor: Julie Grady

Printed in the U.S.A.

TABLE OF CONTENTS

Congratulations, You've Going on a Trip to Boston!

Planning and going on a trip is an exciting adventure. This Kid's Guide and Activity Book is going to help you get ready for, and have loads of fun on, your journey.

What's Inside

Packed inside this book is lots of information about places to see and things to do while you're in Boston as well as entertaining games and activities to get you excited about your trip. Along with fun facts and games there's also plenty of room to record your own memories.

=> Getting Ready for Your Trip

=> Interesting Historical Facts and Sites

=> Top Places to Visit and Things to Do

=> Cool Museums

=> Neighborhoods to Explore

=> Best Ways to Get Around

=> Signature Foods to Try

=> Day Trips

=> Games and Activities

Ready? Let's Go!

PLAN IT OUT

When are we leaving? _____
_____
_____
_____
_____

Who's going? _____
_____
_____
_____

How are we getting there? _____
_____
_____
_____

What I'm most looking forward to: _____
_____
_____
_____

AIRPORT

Word Search

```
S H I R T H S S N E A K E R S
F B Y Q O O R U G H S Z A S F
C H A R G E R U N T Q L U N I
A W P R T C G G R S L H U A B
A L A R O V A O J E C S N C Y
Z B C Q O M H M R O E R H K Q
Z P K G T S W B E H U E E S B
B A I S H T M S T R S R T E J
L N N H B U R O A A A E N Q N
X T G A R D L A C N K B I A T
M S S M U C Z T V C D G V D L
G S V P S F I T A E D A G V U
U Y W O H U V J O Z L Z L X D
B I D O S P A J A M A S Z S E
S U N G L A S S E S Y L U O I
```

CAMERA	PANTS	SUITCASE
CHARGER	SANDALS	SUNGLASSES
CLOTHES	SHAMPOO	SUNSCREEN
JACKET	SHIRT	TOOTHBRUSH
JOURNAL	SHORTS	TRAVEL
PACKING	SNACKS	UMBRELLA
PAJAMAS	SNEAKERS	

PACKING CHECKLIST

CLOTHES

- ☐ T-Shirts
- ☐ Long-sleeved Shirts
- ☐ Sweatshirts and Sweaters
- ☐ Pants
- ☐ Shorts
- ☐ Jacket/Raincoat
- ☐ Underwear
- ☐ Pajamas
- ☐ Socks
- ☐ Bathing Suit/ Cover-Up
- ☐ Sneakers
- ☐ Shoes/Sandals
- ☐ Dressy Outfit
- ☐

PERSONAL ITEMS

- ☐ Soap
- ☐ Toothbrush/Toothpaste/Floss
- ☐ Shampoo/Conditioner
- ☐ Brush/Comb
- ☐ Glasses/Contacts
- ☐

TRAVEL ITEMS

- ☐ Book/Audio Book
- ☐ Drinks/Snacks
- ☐ Charger
- ☐ Phone/Tablet/Camera
- ☐ Headphones
- ☐ Notepad/Journal
- ☐ Pen/Pencil
- ☐ This Guide Book
- ☐

MISCELLANEOUS

- ☐ Sunscreen
- ☐ Umbrella
- ☐ Batteries
- ☐ Hand wipes
- ☐
- ☐
- ☐

A Little Boston History

Boston was founded by Puritan colonists in 1630, making it one of the oldest cities in America.

It became the main commercial, political, and financial center for New England.

Boston played an important part in the American Revolution. In fact, it is referred to as "the birthplace of the American Revolution" because of the many historic events that took place here.

Spiroview Inc / Shutterstock.com

It was the location for the famous Boston Tea Party which took place on December 16, 1773. The Boston Tea Party was a protest by the Sons of Liberty against the British tax on tea. Today you can visit the Boston Tea Party Ships and Museum.

Boston was also the site of the Boston Massacre. This was a riot that occurred in March 1770 to protest the presence of British troops. The troops fired into the crowd and killed five people. This event helped to stir popular opinion against the British.

Some of the first battles of the Revolutionary War took place in and around Boston including the Battle of Bunker Hill and the Battles of Lexington and Concord.

Paul Revere's famous midnight ride in 1775 to warn of the British coming is another famous Revolutionary event that took place in Boston.

In the 19th century Irish immigrants, fleeing the potato famine, made Boston their home.

Another group of famous Bostonians are members of the upper class known as the Boston Brahmins. These were the wealthy descendants of the early English colonists.

BOSTON

Word Scramble

OREDMFE LTRIA	_ _ _ _ _ _ _ _ _ _ _ _
ATETS OHEUS	_ _ _ _ _ _ _ _ _ _
TNSOOB BOHRAR	_ _ _ _ _ _ _ _ _ _ _ _
OBCEAN LHIL	_ _ _ _ _ _ _ _ _ _
AADNSPLEE	_ _ _ _ _ _ _ _
TNIELAUPRD	_ _ _ _ _ _ _ _ _
FUEAILN ALHL	_ _ _ _ _ _ _ _ _ _
ADAHRVR DAYR	_ _ _ _ _ _ _ _ _ _
EHSALRC ERIRV	_ _ _ _ _ _ _ _ _ _ _ _
FEYAWN RAKP	_ _ _ _ _ _ _ _ _ _

Famous Bostonians

Many famous people have called Boston home.

 John Winthrop (1588-1649) – One of the founders of the Massachusetts Bay Colony. Famous for his "City upon a Hill" speech.

 Cotton Mather (1663-1728) – Puritan minister who is famous for his involvement in the Salem witch trials.

 Ben Franklin (1706-1790) – One of the Founding Fathers of the United States. He was a printer, politician, and inventor among other things. He was born in Boston and moved to Philadelphia.

 Paul Revere (1735-1818) – A silversmith, engraver, and Patriot in the American Revolution. Famous for his midnight ride warning of the British coming.

 Ralph Waldo Emerson (1803-1882) – A philosopher and essayist who was one of the founding figures of the transcendentalist movement. .

 Edgar Allen Poe (1809-1849) – An American writer best known for his poems and short stories including "The Raven," "The Cask of Amontillado," and "The Tell-Tale Heart."

 Lucretia Crocker (1829-1886) – Pioneering educator and advocate for higher education for women. First female supervisor of Boston Public Schools.

 John F. Kennedy (1917-1963) – The 35th president of the United States. Youngest man ever elected and first Roman Catholic to be president.

 Sylvia Plath (1932-1963) – One of the most influential poets of the twentieth century.

Mark Wahlberg (1971-present) – Actor, producer, and businessman. Formerly known as Marky Mark.

Getting Around

Walk It!

Boston is a compact city and one of the best ways to explore is to walk! You can get to most places in the city in 20-30 minutes on foot. Plus this is an excellent way to get some exercise and discover those hidden gems.

With so many neighborhoods and parks to explore, you will never get tired of wandering around this fabulous city. Need a break? Relax in the shade on a bench in Boston Common or stop at one of the many sidewalk cafes for a refreshing drink and a bite to eat.

Bike It!

Don't feel like walking? Then rent a bike. There are plenty of bike rental companies in the city, or if you prefer, take a biking tour.

Take the "T"

In Boston, the subway is called the "T" and it is a very convenient way of getting around quickly. It provides access to all the main downtown attractions as well as service to the nearby communities of Cambridge, Brookline, and other nearby suburbs.

f11photo / Shutterstock.com

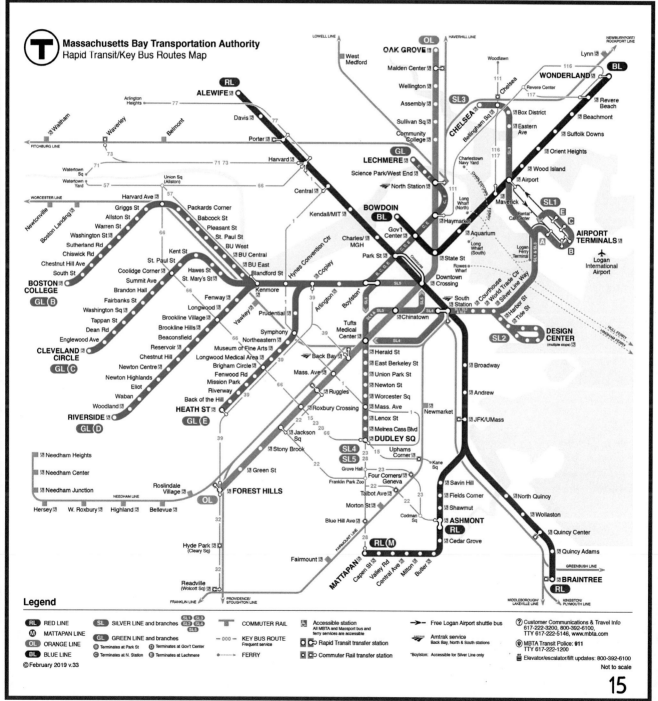

Map of Boston

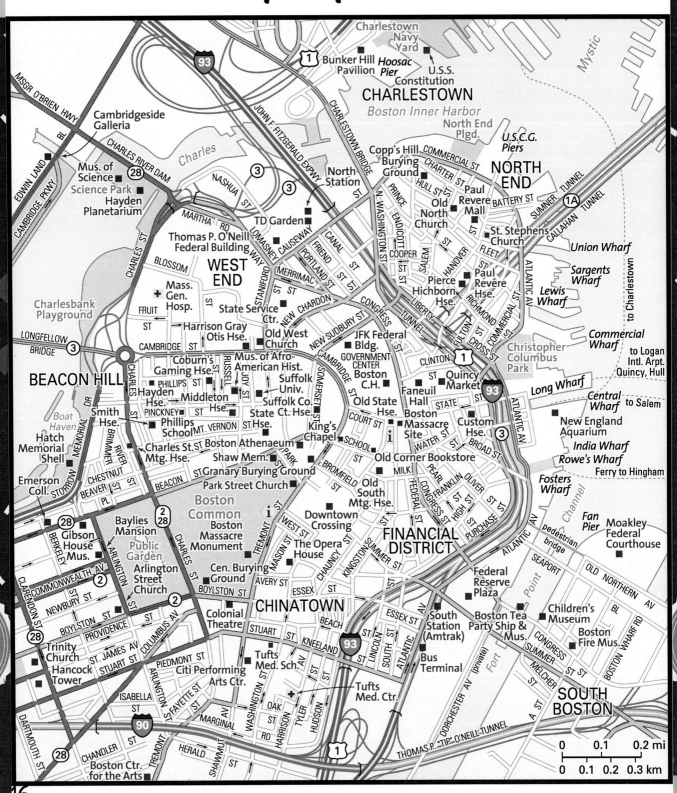

Explore Boston
Geography and Neighborhoods

Boston, aka Beantown, is divided into different neighborhoods, each with a distinctive personality.

Back Bay – This upscale neighborhood centers around the boutique shopping area of Newbury Street.

Jerome LABOUYRIE / Shutterstock.com

Beacon Hill – One of the more historic neighborhoods in Boston, filled with charming walk-up apartments and cobblestone streets.

Charlestown – Just across the Charles River lies this neighborhood, home to Bunker Hill and the USS Constitution.

Downtown Crossing – Right in the city center, this is a busy shopping district as well as a transportation hub.

Mark Zhu / Shutterstock.com

Chinatown – Head over to Chinatown for authentic Chinese cuisine and a bit of culture.

Marcio Jose Bastos Silva / Shutterstock.com

Fenway-Kenmore Square – Take in a game at famous Fenway Park in this neighborhood, which is also home to the Museum of Fine Arts and Symphony Hall.

North End – The Little Italy of Boston, this Italian neighborhood has many historic sites including the Paul Revere House. Stroll around and then enjoy dinner at one of the many authentic Italian restaurants.

Seaport District – This newly revitalized neighborhood is full of delicious restaurants and trendy shops. Like art? Check out the Institute of Contemporary Art. Also home to The Boston Tea Party Ship and Museum and the Children's Museum.

Boston Harbor – Stroll along the Boston HarborWalk and snap some pictures of the amazing views. Here you can catch a whale watch or harbor cruise or visit the New England Aquarium.

Connect the Dots and Color!

21

Top Places to See and Things to Do

Fanueil Hall/Quincy Market – Originally built in 1742, Fanueil Hall was used as a meeting place throughout the 18th and 19th centuries. The adjacent marketplace known as Quincy Market is a popular tourist destination filled with food stalls, restaurants, shops, and exhibitions. Street performers provide free entertainment.

Freedom Trail – Follow the line of red bricks along this 2.5-mile trail past historic sites and monuments including the Old Granary Burying Ground (last resting place of John Hancock, Paul Revere, and Samuel Adams), the Old South Meeting House (Patriots gathered here before the Boston Tea Party), and the old State House (where the Boston Massacre took place).

Boston Common – America's oldest park is located in the center of the city. Stroll around and enjoy the fresh air or perhaps have a picnic. In the summer, enjoy splashing in the wading pool. The Freedom Trail starts here.

USS Constitution – Nicknamed Old Ironsides, the USS Constitution is still a commissioned ship with the U.S. Navy. You can go aboard and see what it's like below the decks. Here you can also visit the USS Constitution Museum and its many interactive exhibits.

New England Aquarium – The New England Aquarium is a must-see attraction for anyone with a love for the ocean and marine life. Get up close and get your hands wet in the touch tanks, wonder at the more than 70 species of tropical fish, or wander through the Amazon rainforest exhibition where you'll see electric eels and poisonous dart frogs. Be sure to catch a film on the big IMAX screen.

Duck Tour – Quack, quack, it's time to ride on one of Boston's famous Duck Tours. Climb aboard this amphibious vehicle and take a narrated sightseeing tour of Boston including a "splashdown" right into the Charles River. You might even get a chance to steer the boat!

Franklin Park Zoo – Everyone will love a visit to the Franklin Park Zoo, located just a few miles from downtown Boston. Open year round, it is home to lions, tigers, gorillas, giraffes, and more. Its many exhibits will teach you about the biodiversity of the planet.

Prudential Tower/Skywalk Observatory – For an unparalleled view of the city head over to the Prudential Center and visit the Skywalk Observatory on the 50th floor for a 360-degree view of all of Boston.

Public Garden/Swan Boats – This 24-acre park is the oldest botanical garden in the United States. Here you can ride the famous Swan Boats, launched in the 1870s.

Copley Square/Newbury Street – On one side of the square is the Boston Public Library, on the other side is the magnificent Trinity Church. Just one block over you can do a little shopping on Newbury Street or stop for a bite to eat at one of the many sidewalk cafes.

Boston Harbor Islands National & State Park – There are 34 Harbor Islands located just off the coast of Boston. Hop on a ferry cruise and explore Spectacle Island with its sandy beaches, hiking trails, and amazing views of the city skyline or head over to Georges Island and check out Fort Warren.

Esplanade – Walk along the Esplanade, a 3-mile stretch of parkway along the Charles River from the Museum of Science to Boston University. The site of the famous Fourth of July fireworks, it also hosts concerts and free movies.

25

Travel Crossword

Across

2. The place you go at the end of your trip.
5. Bring this type of book with you when you travel.
6. A green area in a city for people to enjoy.
8. The place you go to catch a plane.
9. The number of states in the United States.
10. A type of public transportation that is underground.
11. The thing you carry your belongings in when you travel.

Down

1. Say good _____ when you leave.
2. Another word for vacation.
3. Look at this when you are lost to figure out where to go.
4. When you travel by _____ you might run into traffic.
7. Mode of transportation to get from place to place fast.

Find the Travel Icons in the Picture

Museums

Want to learn something and have fun doing it?
Check out these top museums in Boston.

Museum of Science – With over 500 exhibits, the Boston Museum of Science has something for everyone in the family to enjoy. See a laser show, get transported to outer space in the planetarium, wander through a butterfly garden, or get an up-close view of a giant triceratops—you are sure to learn a lot and have fun doing it.

James Kirakis / Shutterstock.com

f11photo / Shutterstock.com

Boston Children's Museum – Head on over to the Boston Children's Museum for a day of fun! Make giant soap bubbles, learn about the laws of physics, and navigate your way through a two-story maze.

John F. Kennedy Presidential Library and Museum – Located on the waterfront in the Dorchester neighborhood of Boston, this is the presidential library and museum of the 35th president of the United States. See a film about the life of JFK and then explore the exhibits, photographs, and memorabilia including Jacqueline Kennedy's wardrobe, the space race, the Cuban Missile Crisis, and members of the Kennedy family.

Marcio Jose Bastos Silva / Shutterstock.com

Harvard Museum of Natural History –

Head on over to Cambridge and experience the wonders of the natural world. Exhibits include evolution, animals of the world, climate change, planets, and more.

Papa Bravo / Shutterstock.com

Boston Tea Party Ships and Museum –

Climb aboard this restored tall ship and reenact the famous Boston Tea Party and then head inside the museum to experience its high-tech and interactive exhibits. Experience a hands-on chance to learn about the events leading to the American Revolution.

Museum of Fine Arts –

Features some of the most famous works of art in the world including pieces by Picasso and Leonardo Da Vinci. See ancient Egyptian art including mummies, the Monet gallery, a collection of ancient coins, arts and crafts from the Americas, and much more. The museum also hosts many hands-on events for kids.

Osugi / Shutterstock.com

Trip to the Museum Word Search

```
E B G A H I S T O R Y V R S Z T I S I V
M S K Q R Z J W A T P J O D I R T C K F
E S O R Q C D Q X A G R L Q I B Y A B U
E O H Y V C H L W P U E E K T O E K A D
C Q J N T Y C I M K I X M S M A E Z S O
N T O O E S L I V Z D H U Y E S F U C V
E S A I D G P A Q E E I E J B R D Y Z G
I W R S G A T S C F S B S I E G V N Y W
C V T S F P W M O V S I U P G S C E W G
S V I I O G H T L D R T M L G Z E G N K
X D F M S M U I R A T E N A L P E I V E
Z P A D S B P N G M Q G I I D U T F D W
U O C A I D W T Y L N D D N E N M Y P E
S I T P L G D F I O L R L E I H K O A R
Y C S I S L M O Y C U D T A V S H C O Z
K O B A E H B P T A K V P Q D S T T L B
A R T I S T M C T J T E N U T M A O S T
C O L L E C T I O N Z I T F E R T F U D
N T T G W Q Z V K Q Y D I F U O W C I R
O O I G N I N R A E L G R C D M D D P U
```

ADMISSION	CURATOR	HISTORY	PRESERVE
ARCHIVES	EXHIBIT	LEARNING	SCIENCE
ARTIFACTS	FOSSILS	MUSEUM	TICKET
ARTIST	GIFT SHOP	PAINTING	TOUR
COLLECTION	GUIDE	PLANETARIUM	VISIT

Isabella Stewart Gardner Museum – A beautiful gem tucked away in the Fens area of Boston, this museum is the former home of art collector Isabella Stewart Gardner. Modeled after a Venetian palazzo, it features a lush courtyard area.

Institute of Contemporary Art – Located in the Seaport District of the city, this museum features all types of contemporary art including visual art, film, music, and performance. A great place to experience newer artists.

MIT Museum – This museum focuses on technology and innovation. Exhibits feature science, technology, and inventions. Learn about computers, holograms, kinetic art, and other STEAM-related topics.

Sports Town!

Boston is a sports town and there's nothing Bostonians love more than rooting for their favorite teams. If you can while you are visiting go to a game. Depending on the season, head over to Fenway Park and see the Red Sox play, go to a Celtics' or Bruins' game at TD Garden, or take a drive to Foxboro to watch the New England Patriots.

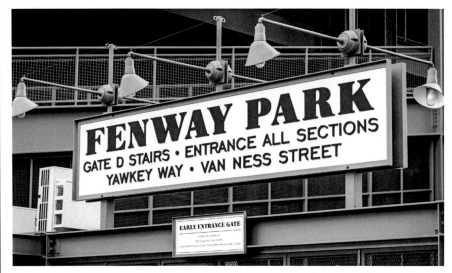

Fenway Park has been the home of the Boston Red Sox since 1912. The Green Monster is the nickname given to the left field wall.

Both the Boston Celtics and the Boston Bruins play at TD Garden.

Gillette Stadium, located about 30 miles from Boston in Foxborough, is where you can see the New England Patriots play football.

Jai Agnish / Shutterstock.com

Richard Cavalleri / Shutterstock.com

littlenySTOCK / Shutterstock.com

Sports Trivia

1. Where is the basketball hall of fame located? _____

2. For what team did Babe Ruth play for? _____

3. In what sport is the Stanley Cup given out? _____

4. What year was baseball invented in? _____

5. Where is Fenway Park located? _____

6. What is the original home of the LA Dodgers? _____

7. Which sport does not use a ball? _____

8. What city hosted the 2002 Winter Olympics? _____

9. What three events are in a triathlon? _____

10. How long is a marathon? _____

11. Which sports play on a court? _____

12. In what sport do you need a caddy? _____

13. The Tour de France is what type of event? _____

14. What is another name for ping pong? _____

See Some Historic Sites

Old North Church – Located in the North End, the Old North Church was built in 1723. Many soldiers killed in the battle of Bunker Hill are buried in its crypt.

Old State House – Built in 1713, the Old State House is one of the oldest public buildings in the United States. This National Historic Landmark is now a museum and hosts daily tours.

Trinity Church – This beautiful Romanesque-style church anchors Copley Square. Built in the 1870s, it is still used as a church with several services each week.

King's Chapel Burying Ground – This historic graveyard on Tremont Street is the oldest cemetery in Boston. There are more than 500 people buried here including Mary Chilton, the first European woman to step foot in New England and John Winthrop, the first Puritan governor of Massachusetts.

Bunker Hill Monument – Site of the first major battle of the American Revolution. The battle took place on June 17, 1775 and the Patriots lost to the British.

Old South Meeting House – Built in 1729, the Old South Meeting house was almost destroyed in the Great Boston Fire of 1872. The Boston Tea Party was organized here.

Paul Revere House – Tour the former home of Revolutionary Patriot Paul Revere. Built in 1680, it's the oldest house in downtown Boston.

Eat Like a Bostonian

When in Boston be sure to try some of the signature dishes that it is known for like fresh seafood and spectacular desserts.

New England Clam Chowder is a classic that can be found at just about any restaurant in the city. Creamy and delicious!

Nothing beats crispy, golden, **fried scrod** eaten down by the waterfront on Boston Harbor. Delicious with french fries and tartar sauce.

Head over to Fenway Park and enjoy a famous **Fenway Frank** while you watch a game.

Boston's nickname, Beantown, is based on these famous **baked beans.**

You might think of Maine when it comes to lobster, but getting a **lobster roll** is a Boston treat you will not want to miss.

Boston has no shortage of **pizza** restaurants where you can get a tantalizing slice of pie. Regina Pizzeria has been dishing out tasty slices since 1926.

Boston is known for its seafood and **oysters** are considered a delicacy. Eat them raw, on the half shell, with just a squeeze of lemon.

Head over to the North End for some delicious Italian food and be sure to top it off with a mouth-watering **cannoli**. Get one at the famous Mike's Pastry on Hanover Street.

Boston Cream Pie is the official dessert of Massachusetts and when you're in Boston you've got to try it. Creamy and chocolately, this rich dessert has been a favorite since 1856.

Parks and Playgrounds

When you need a little break, head over to one of Boston's many parks and playgrounds to relax, run around, and let off some steam.

=> **Tadpole Playground:** In the middle of Boston Common is the Tadpole Playground. Here you will find plenty of climbing structures, monkey bars, and swings. In the summer you can run through the sprinklers or wade through Frog Pond. In the winter you can ice skate.

=> **Esplanade**: The Esplanade contains three playgrounds, the Esplanade Playspace, the Stoneman Playground, and the Charlesbank Playground. Each features a variety of climbing structures, swings, slides, tunnels, and even a zip line.

=> **Christopher Columbus Park:** Located along the waterfront near Boston's North End is this large playground and park. This park has climbing structures, a sandbox, and a rose garden. Across the street is the Greenway Carousel.

=> **Thomas M. Menino Park:** An inclusive playground with views of the Charles River, this playspace in Charlestown features climbing structures, swings, and monkey bars. Designed for the needs of all children.

Day Trips

If you have time while in the Boston area, check out some of these amazing places that are only a short distance away.

Salem – The town of Salem is located approximately 35 minutes north of Boston. It's famous for being the site of the Salem Witch Trials, held in 1692. Today, visitors can get a sense of this history by visiting the Salem Witch Museum or taking a guided walking tour.

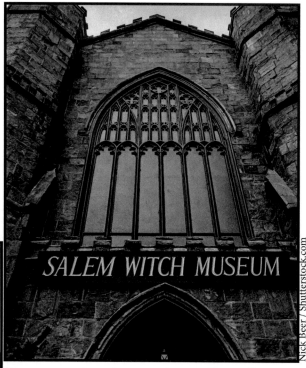

SALEM WITCH MUSEUM

Nick Beer / Shutterstock.com

Portsmouth – Just an hour from Boston is the idyllic coastal town of Portsmouth, New Hampshire. Filled with historic homes, parks, museums, and beaches, it makes for an interesting day trip. For those looking to get wet, this is also where you can find the largest water park in New England, Water Country.

Whale Watch – Whale watch cruises leave from Boston Harbor on half-day tours. Cruises head out to Stellwagen Bank National Marine Sanctuary to find whales, dolphins, porpoises, and other marine life. Most cruises have a naturalist aboard to explain about the whales and other species found in the ocean.

Provincetown – Located at the very tip of Cape Cod, Provincetown is known as an artist colony. Visit Pilgrim Monument, the spot where Pilgrims first landed. Stroll down Commercial Street and visit the many art galleries, eclectic boutiques, and ice cream shops. Provincetown is a 2-hour car ride from Boston or can be reached by ferry from Boston Harbor.

Lexington and Concord – These two towns are famous for their roles in the Revolutionary War. Visitors today can visit the battle sites, cemeteries, and memorials which commemorate the soldiers who fought in the American Revolution. The towns are located 30 minutes outside of Boston.

Plimoth Plantation – Spend a day soaking up history in this living museum located 50 minutes south of Boston. Here you can learn about the day-to-day life of early colonists, visit the Mayflower II, and see a Wampanoag homesite.

Crossword Trivia

Across

3. How many Great Lakes are there?
5. Where does the president live?
6. America's national past time.
9. Where did the Pilgrims first land?
11. In what state was gold first found?
12. Abraham Lincoln was the _____ president.
13. What country gave the Statue of Liberty to America?

Down

1. The longest river in the United States.
2. What state is known as the Lone Star State?
4. The Liberty Bell is located in _____
7. Walt Disney's most famous character.
8. A cold delicious treat on a hot day.
10. Where is Disney World located?

Favorite Memory

Draw a picture of your favorite memory of the trip.

Trip Journal

Trip Journal

Trip Journal

Trip Journal

Welcome to MASSACHUSETTS

atlantic ocean
nantucket
cape cod bay
martha's vineyard
buzzards bay
cape ann
BOSTON
FALL RIVER
CAMBRIDGE
WORCESTER
Quabbin Reservoir
SPRINGFIELD

Answers to Puzzles and Games

Across
2. The place you go at the end of your trip.
5. Bring this type of book with you when you travel.
6. A green area in a city for people to enjoy.
8. The place you go to catch a plane.
9. The number of states in the United States.
10. A type of public transportation that is underground.
11. The thing you carry your belongings in when you travel.

Down
1. Say good _____ when you leave.
2. Another word for vacation.
3. Look at this when you are lost to figure out where to go.
4. When you travel by _____ you might run into traffic.
7. Mode of transportation to get from place to place fast.

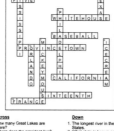

Across
3. How many Great Lakes are there?
5. Where does the president live?
6. America's national past time.
9. Where did the Pilgrims first land?
11. In what state was gold first found?
12. Abraham Lincoln was the president.
13. What country gave the Statue of Liberty to America?

Down
1. The longest river in the United States.
2. What state is known as the Lone Star State?
4. The Liberty Bell is located in _____.
7. Walt Disney's most famous character.
8. A cold delicious treat on a hot day.
10. Where is Disney World located?

1. SPRINGFIELD, MASS.
2. YANKEES
3. HOCKEY
4. 1869
5. BOSTON
6. BROOKLYN, NY
7. HOCKEY
8. SALT LAKE CITY
9. BIKING, SWIMMING, RUNNING
10. 26.2 MILES
11. BASKETBALL, TENNIS
12. GOLF
13. BIKE RACE
14. TABLE TENNIS

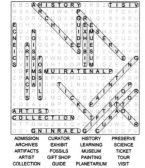

ADMISSION   CURATOR   HISTORY   PRESERVE
ARCHIVES   EXHIBIT   LEARNING   SCIENCE
ARTIFACTS   FOSSILS   MUSEUM   TICKET
ARTIST   GIFT SHOP PAINTING   TOUR
COLLECTION   GUIDE   PLANETARIUM VISIT

CAMERA   PANTS   SUITCASE
CHARGER   SANDALS   SUNGLASSES
CLOTHES   SHAMPOO   SUNSCREEN
JACKET   SHIRT   TOOTHBRUSH
JOURNAL   SHORTS   TRAVEL
PACKING   SNACKS   UMBRELLA
PAJAMAS   SNEAKERS

1. OREDMFE LTRIA — F r e e d o m   T r a i l
2. ATETS OHEUS — S t a t e   H o u s e
3. TNSOOB BOHRAR — B o s t o n   H a r b o r
4. OBCEAN LHIL — B e a c o n   H i l l
5. AADNSPLEE — E s p l a n a d e
6. TNIELAUPRD — P r u d e n t i a l
7. FUEAILN ALHL — F a n u e i l   H a l l
8. ADAHRVR DAYR — H a r v a r d   Y a r d
9. EHSALRC ERIRV — C h a r l e s   R i v e r
10. FEYAWN RAKP — F e n w a y   P a r k

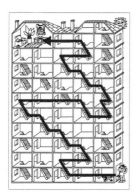

Made in the USA
San Bernardino, CA
22 June 2019